D0286463

DIVE LOG BOOK

THIS   LOG BOOK BELONGS TO:

Name:

Address:

Phone:

In case of emergency, please contact:

DIVE NO

DATE

DIVE GROUP

WEATHER CONDITIONS

WEATHER CONDITIONS

START
bar / psi

END
bar / psi

LOCATION

TIME IN

TIME OUT

:

:

DIVE TIME

:

AVERAGE DEPTH

MAX DEPTH

LOCATION

LOCATION NAME

COUNTRY

EQUIPMENT

ADDITIONAL NOTES

DIVE CENTER / RESORT STAMP

INSTRUCTOR

AI / DM

BUDDY

DIVE NO

DATE

DIVE GROUP

WEATHER CONDITIONS

START bar / psi	END bar / psi
_____	_____

LOCATION

TIME IN

:

TIME OUT

:

DIVE TIME

:

AVERAGE DEPTH

MAX DEPTH

WEATHER CONDITIONS

_____

_____

LOCATION

LOCATION NAME

COUNTRY

EQUIPMENT

ADDITIONAL NOTES

DIVE CENTER / RESORT STAMP

INSTRUCTOR

AI / DM

BUDDY

DIVE NO

DATE

DIVE GROUP

WEATHER CONDITIONS

	START bar / psi		END bar / psi
	_____		_____

LOCATION

TIME IN

TIME OUT

:

:

DIVE TIME

:

AVERAGE DEPTH

MAX DEPTH

ADDITIONAL NOTES

WEATHER CONDITIONS

_____

☐ ☐ ☐ ☐ ☐

LOCATION

LOCATION NAME

COUNTRY

EQUIPMENT

DIVE CENTER / RESORT STAMP

INSTRUCTOR ☐ AI / DM ☐ BUDDY ☐

DIVE NO

DATE

DIVE GROUP

WEATHER CONDITIONS

WEATHER CONDITIONS

START
bar / psi

END
bar / psi

LOCATION

LOCATION NAME

COUNTRY

LOCATION

TIME IN

TIME OUT

:

:

DIVE TIME

:

AVERAGE DEPTH

MAX DEPTH

EQUIPMENT

ADDITIONAL NOTES

DIVE CENTER / RESORT STAMP

INSTRUCTOR

AI / DM

BUDDY

DIVE NO

DATE

DIVE GROUP

WEATHER CONDITIONS

WEATHER CONDITIONS

START
bar / psi

END
bar / psi

LOCATION

TIME IN

TIME OUT

:

:

DIVE TIME

:

AVERAGE DEPTH

MAX DEPTH

LOCATION

LOCATION NAME

COUNTRY

EQUIPMENT

ADDITIONAL NOTES

DIVE CENTER / RESORT STAMP

INSTRUCTOR

AI / DM

BUDDY

DIVE NO

DATE

DIVE GROUP

WEATHER CONDITIONS

Temperature: _____

Wind: _____

WEATHER CONDITIONS

START bar / psi	END bar / psi
_____	_____

LOCATION

TIME IN :   TIME OUT :

DIVE TIME :

AVERAGE DEPTH

MAX DEPTH

LOCATION

LOCATION NAME

COUNTRY

EQUIPMENT

ADDITIONAL NOTES

DIVE CENTER / RESORT STAMP

INSTRUCTOR   AI / DM   BUDDY

DIVE NO

DATE

DIVE GROUP

WEATHER CONDITIONS

START
bar / psi

END
bar / psi

LOCATION

TIME IN

TIME OUT

DIVE TIME

AVERAGE DEPTH

MAX DEPTH

WEATHER CONDITIONS

LOCATION

LOCATION NAME

COUNTRY

EQUIPMENT

ADDITIONAL NOTES

DIVE CENTER / RESORT STAMP

INSTRUCTOR

AI / DM

BUDDY

DIVE NO

DATE

DIVE GROUP

WEATHER CONDITIONS

WEATHER CONDITIONS

START bar / psi

END bar / psi

LOCATION

LOCATION NAME

COUNTRY

LOCATION

TIME IN

TIME OUT

DIVE TIME

AVERAGE DEPTH

MAX DEPTH

EQUIPMENT

ADDITIONAL NOTES

DIVE CENTER / RESORT STAMP

INSTRUCTOR

AI / DM

BUDDY

DIVE NO

DATE

DIVE GROUP

WEATHER CONDITIONS

☼ ⛅ ☁ 🌧 ❄

WEATHER CONDITIONS

START bar / psi	END bar / psi
_____	_____

LOCATION

LOCATION NAME

COUNTRY

LOCATION

TIME IN   TIME OUT
:   :

DIVE TIME
:

AVERAGE DEPTH

MAX DEPTH

EQUIPMENT

ADDITIONAL NOTES

DIVE CENTER / RESORT STAMP

INSTRUCTOR   AI / DM   BUDDY
☐   ☐   ☐

DIVE NO

DATE

DIVE GROUP

WEATHER CONDITIONS

WEATHER CONDITIONS

START
bar / psi

END
bar / psi

LOCATION

TIME IN

TIME OUT

:

:

DIVE TIME

:

AVERAGE DEPTH

MAX DEPTH

LOCATION

LOCATION NAME

COUNTRY

EQUIPMENT

ADDITIONAL NOTES

DIVE CENTER / RESORT STAMP

INSTRUCTOR

AI / DM

BUDDY

DIVE NO

DATE

DIVE GROUP

WEATHER CONDITIONS

___ ☀ ⛅ 🌧 ⛈ ❄

___ ☐ ☐ ☐ ☐ ☐

WEATHER CONDITIONS

START
bar / psi

_____

END
bar / psi

_____

LOCATION

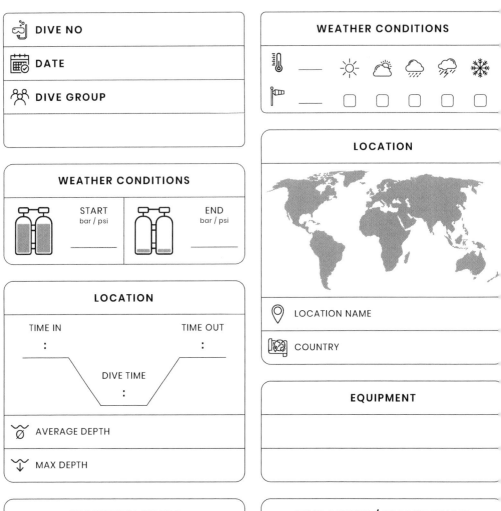

LOCATION NAME

COUNTRY

LOCATION

TIME IN

:

TIME OUT

:

DIVE TIME

:

AVERAGE DEPTH

MAX DEPTH

EQUIPMENT

ADDITIONAL NOTES

DIVE CENTER / RESORT STAMP

INSTRUCTOR

☐

AI / DM

☐

BUDDY

☐

DIVE NO

DATE

DIVE GROUP

WEATHER CONDITIONS

START
bar / psi

END
bar / psi

WEATHER CONDITIONS

LOCATION

TIME IN

TIME OUT

:

:

DIVE TIME

:

AVERAGE DEPTH

MAX DEPTH

LOCATION

LOCATION NAME

COUNTRY

EQUIPMENT

ADDITIONAL NOTES

DIVE CENTER / RESORT STAMP

INSTRUCTOR

AI / DM

BUDDY

DIVE NO

DATE

DIVE GROUP

WEATHER CONDITIONS

WEATHER CONDITIONS

START
bar / psi

_____

END
bar / psi

_____

LOCATION

LOCATION NAME

COUNTRY

LOCATION

TIME IN

:

TIME OUT

:

DIVE TIME

:

AVERAGE DEPTH

MAX DEPTH

EQUIPMENT

ADDITIONAL NOTES

DIVE CENTER / RESORT STAMP

INSTRUCTOR

AI / DM

BUDDY

DIVE NO

DATE

DIVE GROUP

WEATHER CONDITIONS

WEATHER CONDITIONS

START
bar / psi

END
bar / psi

LOCATION

LOCATION NAME

COUNTRY

LOCATION

TIME IN

TIME OUT

:

:

DIVE TIME

:

AVERAGE DEPTH

MAX DEPTH

EQUIPMENT

ADDITIONAL NOTES

DIVE CENTER / RESORT STAMP

INSTRUCTOR   AI / DM   BUDDY

DIVE NO

DATE

DIVE GROUP

WEATHER CONDITIONS

START
bar / psi
_____

END
bar / psi
_____

WEATHER CONDITIONS

LOCATION

TIME IN

TIME OUT

:

:

DIVE TIME

:

AVERAGE DEPTH

MAX DEPTH

ADDITIONAL NOTES

WEATHER CONDITIONS

_____

_____

LOCATION

LOCATION NAME

COUNTRY

EQUIPMENT

DIVE CENTER / RESORT STAMP

INSTRUCTOR   AI / DM   BUDDY

DIVE NO

DATE

DIVE GROUP

WEATHER CONDITIONS

WEATHER CONDITIONS

START
bar / psi

END
bar / psi

LOCATION

LOCATION NAME

COUNTRY

LOCATION

TIME IN

TIME OUT

:

:

DIVE TIME

:

AVERAGE DEPTH

MAX DEPTH

EQUIPMENT

ADDITIONAL NOTES

DIVE CENTER / RESORT STAMP

INSTRUCTOR   AI / DM   BUDDY

DIVE NO

DATE

DIVE GROUP

WEATHER CONDITIONS

START	END
bar / psi	bar / psi
_____	_____

LOCATION

TIME IN   TIME OUT
:   :

DIVE TIME
:

AVERAGE DEPTH

MAX DEPTH

ADDITIONAL NOTES

WEATHER CONDITIONS

LOCATION

LOCATION NAME

COUNTRY

EQUIPMENT

DIVE CENTER / RESORT STAMP

INSTRUCTOR   AI / DM   BUDDY

DIVE NO

DATE

DIVE GROUP

WEATHER CONDITIONS

—					
—					

WEATHER CONDITIONS

START bar / psi	END bar / psi
_____	_____

LOCATION

LOCATION NAME

COUNTRY

LOCATION

TIME IN :   TIME OUT :

DIVE TIME :

AVERAGE DEPTH

MAX DEPTH

EQUIPMENT

ADDITIONAL NOTES

DIVE CENTER / RESORT STAMP

INSTRUCTOR   AI / DM   BUDDY

DIVE NO

DATE

DIVE GROUP

WEATHER CONDITIONS

WEATHER CONDITIONS

START
bar / psi

END
bar / psi

LOCATION

TIME IN

TIME OUT

:

:

DIVE TIME

:

AVERAGE DEPTH

MAX DEPTH

LOCATION

LOCATION NAME

COUNTRY

EQUIPMENT

ADDITIONAL NOTES

DIVE CENTER / RESORT STAMP

INSTRUCTOR

AI / DM

BUDDY

DIVE NO

DATE

DIVE GROUP

WEATHER CONDITIONS

WEATHER CONDITIONS

START
bar / psi

END
bar / psi

LOCATION

TIME IN

TIME OUT

:

:

DIVE TIME

:

AVERAGE DEPTH

MAX DEPTH

LOCATION

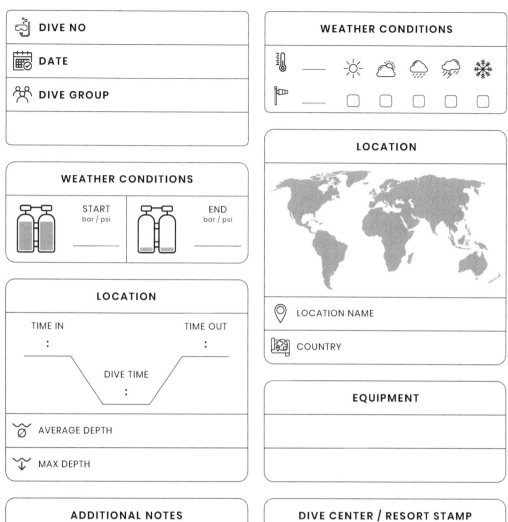

LOCATION NAME

COUNTRY

EQUIPMENT

ADDITIONAL NOTES

DIVE CENTER / RESORT STAMP

INSTRUCTOR   AI / DM   BUDDY

DIVE NO

DATE

DIVE GROUP

WEATHER CONDITIONS

START
bar / psi

END
bar / psi

LOCATION

TIME IN

TIME OUT

:

:

DIVE TIME

:

AVERAGE DEPTH

MAX DEPTH

ADDITIONAL NOTES

WEATHER CONDITIONS

LOCATION

LOCATION NAME

COUNTRY

EQUIPMENT

DIVE CENTER / RESORT STAMP

INSTRUCTOR

AI / DM

BUDDY

DIVE NO

DATE

DIVE GROUP

WEATHER CONDITIONS

☀ ⛅ 🌧 ⛈ ❄

WEATHER CONDITIONS

START
bar / psi

END
bar / psi

LOCATION

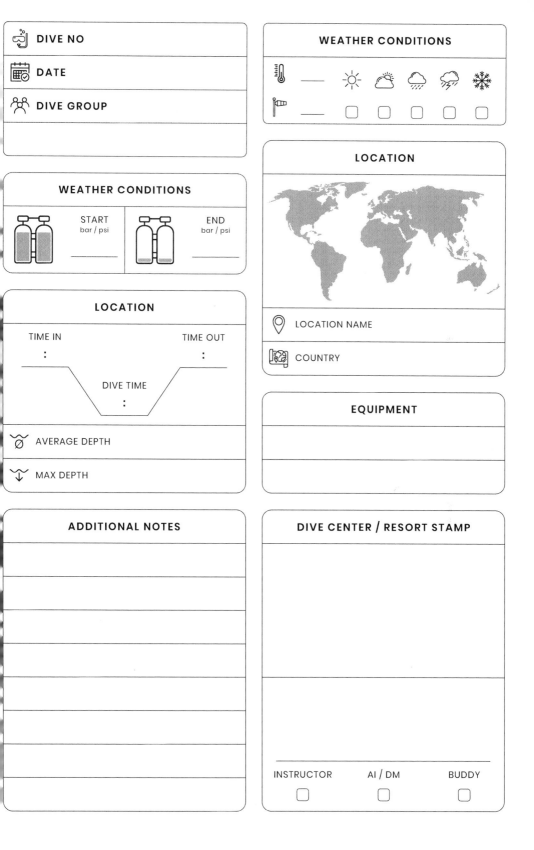

LOCATION NAME

COUNTRY

LOCATION

TIME IN

TIME OUT

:

:

DIVE TIME

:

AVERAGE DEPTH

MAX DEPTH

EQUIPMENT

ADDITIONAL NOTES

DIVE CENTER / RESORT STAMP

INSTRUCTOR   AI / DM   BUDDY

DIVE NO

DATE

DIVE GROUP

WEATHER CONDITIONS

START
bar / psi

END
bar / psi

LOCATION

TIME IN

TIME OUT

:

:

DIVE TIME

:

AVERAGE DEPTH

MAX DEPTH

WEATHER CONDITIONS

LOCATION

LOCATION NAME

COUNTRY

EQUIPMENT

ADDITIONAL NOTES

DIVE CENTER / RESORT STAMP

INSTRUCTOR

AI / DM

BUDDY

DIVE NO

DATE

DIVE GROUP

WEATHER CONDITIONS

WEATHER CONDITIONS

START bar / psi	END bar / psi

LOCATION

TIME IN

TIME OUT

:

:

DIVE TIME

:

AVERAGE DEPTH

MAX DEPTH

LOCATION

LOCATION NAME

COUNTRY

EQUIPMENT

ADDITIONAL NOTES

DIVE CENTER / RESORT STAMP

INSTRUCTOR   AI / DM   BUDDY

DIVE NO

DATE

DIVE GROUP

WEATHER CONDITIONS

WEATHER CONDITIONS

START
bar / psi

END
bar / psi

LOCATION

LOCATION NAME

COUNTRY

LOCATION

TIME IN

TIME OUT

:

:

DIVE TIME

:

AVERAGE DEPTH

MAX DEPTH

EQUIPMENT

ADDITIONAL NOTES

DIVE CENTER / RESORT STAMP

INSTRUCTOR

AI / DM

BUDDY

DIVE NO

DATE

DIVE GROUP

WEATHER CONDITIONS

START
bar / psi

END
bar / psi

LOCATION

TIME IN

TIME OUT

:

:

DIVE TIME

:

AVERAGE DEPTH

MAX DEPTH

WEATHER CONDITIONS

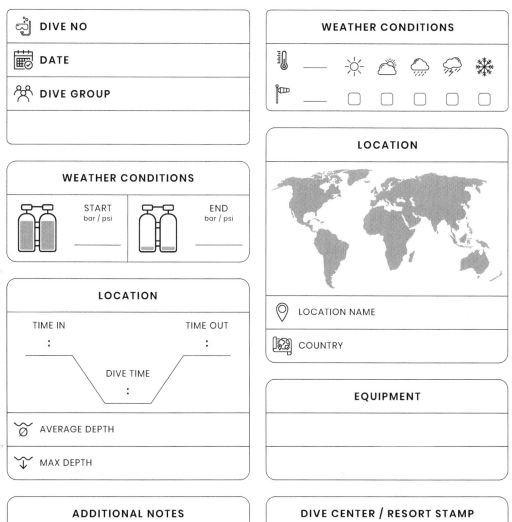

LOCATION

LOCATION NAME

COUNTRY

EQUIPMENT

ADDITIONAL NOTES

DIVE CENTER / RESORT STAMP

INSTRUCTOR   AI / DM   BUDDY

DIVE NO

DATE

DIVE GROUP

WEATHER CONDITIONS

—

—

WEATHER CONDITIONS

START bar / psi	END bar / psi
_____	_____

LOCATION

TIME IN

:

TIME OUT

:

DIVE TIME

:

AVERAGE DEPTH

MAX DEPTH

LOCATION

LOCATION NAME

COUNTRY

EQUIPMENT

ADDITIONAL NOTES

DIVE CENTER / RESORT STAMP

INSTRUCTOR   AI / DM   BUDDY

DIVE NO

DATE

DIVE GROUP

WEATHER CONDITIONS

START bar / psi	END bar / psi

LOCATION

TIME IN

TIME OUT

:

:

DIVE TIME

:

AVERAGE DEPTH

MAX DEPTH

ADDITIONAL NOTES

WEATHER CONDITIONS

LOCATION

LOCATION NAME

COUNTRY

EQUIPMENT

DIVE CENTER / RESORT STAMP

INSTRUCTOR   AI / DM   BUDDY

DIVE NO

DATE

DIVE GROUP

WEATHER CONDITIONS

🌡 ———

💨 ———

☀ ⛅ 🌧 ⛈ ❄

☐ ☐ ☐ ☐ ☐

WEATHER CONDITIONS

START bar / psi	END bar / psi
_____	_____

LOCATION

📍 LOCATION NAME

🗺 COUNTRY

LOCATION

TIME IN   TIME OUT

:   :

DIVE TIME

:

⌀ AVERAGE DEPTH

↓ MAX DEPTH

EQUIPMENT

ADDITIONAL NOTES

DIVE CENTER / RESORT STAMP

INSTRUCTOR   AI / DM   BUDDY

☐   ☐   ☐

DIVE NO

DATE

DIVE GROUP

WEATHER CONDITIONS

🌡️ ____	☀️ ⛅ 🌧️ ⛈️ ❄️
🚩 ____	☐ ☐ ☐ ☐ ☐

WEATHER CONDITIONS

START bar / psi	END bar / psi
____	____

LOCATION

📍 LOCATION NAME

🗺️ COUNTRY

LOCATION

TIME IN

:

TIME OUT

:

DIVE TIME

:

AVERAGE DEPTH

MAX DEPTH

EQUIPMENT

ADDITIONAL NOTES

DIVE CENTER / RESORT STAMP

INSTRUCTOR	AI / DM	BUDDY
☐	☐	☐

DIVE NO

DATE

DIVE GROUP

WEATHER CONDITIONS

WEATHER CONDITIONS

START
bar / psi

END
bar / psi

LOCATION

LOCATION NAME

COUNTRY

LOCATION

TIME IN

TIME OUT

:

:

DIVE TIME

:

AVERAGE DEPTH

MAX DEPTH

EQUIPMENT

ADDITIONAL NOTES

DIVE CENTER / RESORT STAMP

INSTRUCTOR

AI / DM

BUDDY

DIVE NO

DATE

DIVE GROUP

WEATHER CONDITIONS

	START bar / psi		END bar / psi

LOCATION

TIME IN	TIME OUT
:	:

DIVE TIME

:

AVERAGE DEPTH

MAX DEPTH

WEATHER CONDITIONS

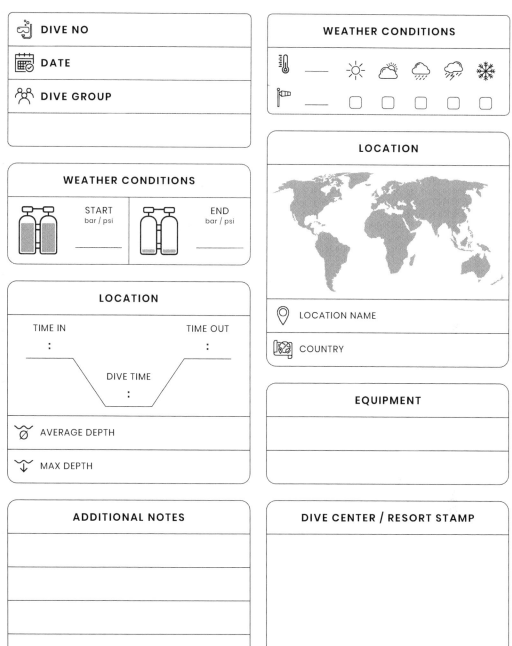

LOCATION

LOCATION NAME

COUNTRY

EQUIPMENT

ADDITIONAL NOTES

DIVE CENTER / RESORT STAMP

INSTRUCTOR	AI / DM	BUDDY

DIVE NO

DATE

DIVE GROUP

WEATHER CONDITIONS

START bar / psi	END bar / psi

LOCATION

TIME IN

:

TIME OUT

:

DIVE TIME

:

AVERAGE DEPTH

MAX DEPTH

ADDITIONAL NOTES

WEATHER CONDITIONS

LOCATION

LOCATION NAME

COUNTRY

EQUIPMENT

DIVE CENTER / RESORT STAMP

INSTRUCTOR   AI / DM   BUDDY

DIVE NO

DATE

DIVE GROUP

WEATHER CONDITIONS

WEATHER CONDITIONS

START bar / psi	END bar / psi

LOCATION

TIME IN

TIME OUT

:

:

DIVE TIME

:

AVERAGE DEPTH

MAX DEPTH

LOCATION

LOCATION NAME

COUNTRY

EQUIPMENT

ADDITIONAL NOTES

DIVE CENTER / RESORT STAMP

INSTRUCTOR   AI / DM   BUDDY

DIVE NO

DATE

DIVE GROUP

WEATHER CONDITIONS

START bar / psi	END bar / psi

LOCATION

TIME IN

TIME OUT

:

:

DIVE TIME

:

AVERAGE DEPTH

MAX DEPTH

ADDITIONAL NOTES

WEATHER CONDITIONS

LOCATION

LOCATION NAME

COUNTRY

EQUIPMENT

DIVE CENTER / RESORT STAMP

INSTRUCTOR   AI / DM   BUDDY

DIVE NO

DATE

DIVE GROUP

WEATHER CONDITIONS

START
bar / psi

END
bar / psi

LOCATION

TIME IN

TIME OUT

:

:

DIVE TIME

:

AVERAGE DEPTH

MAX DEPTH

WEATHER CONDITIONS

LOCATION

LOCATION NAME

COUNTRY

EQUIPMENT

ADDITIONAL NOTES

DIVE CENTER / RESORT STAMP

INSTRUCTOR

AI / DM

BUDDY

DIVE NO

DATE

DIVE GROUP

WEATHER CONDITIONS

WEATHER CONDITIONS

START
bar / psi

_____

END
bar / psi

_____

LOCATION

○ LOCATION NAME

COUNTRY

LOCATION

TIME IN

:

TIME OUT

:

DIVE TIME

:

AVERAGE DEPTH

MAX DEPTH

EQUIPMENT

ADDITIONAL NOTES

DIVE CENTER / RESORT STAMP

INSTRUCTOR

AI / DM

BUDDY

DIVE NO

DATE

DIVE GROUP

WEATHER CONDITIONS

START
bar / psi

END
bar / psi

LOCATION

TIME IN

TIME OUT

:

:

DIVE TIME

:

AVERAGE DEPTH

MAX DEPTH

WEATHER CONDITIONS

LOCATION

LOCATION NAME

COUNTRY

EQUIPMENT

ADDITIONAL NOTES

DIVE CENTER / RESORT STAMP

INSTRUCTOR

AI / DM

BUDDY

DIVE NO

DATE

DIVE GROUP

WEATHER CONDITIONS

START
bar / psi

END
bar / psi

WEATHER CONDITIONS

LOCATION

LOCATION NAME

COUNTRY

LOCATION

TIME IN

TIME OUT

:

:

DIVE TIME

:

AVERAGE DEPTH

MAX DEPTH

EQUIPMENT

ADDITIONAL NOTES

DIVE CENTER / RESORT STAMP

INSTRUCTOR

AI / DM

BUDDY

DIVE NO

DATE

DIVE GROUP

WEATHER CONDITIONS

WEATHER CONDITIONS

START
bar / psi

END
bar / psi

LOCATION

LOCATION NAME

COUNTRY

LOCATION

TIME IN

TIME OUT

:

:

DIVE TIME

:

AVERAGE DEPTH

MAX DEPTH

EQUIPMENT

ADDITIONAL NOTES

DIVE CENTER / RESORT STAMP

INSTRUCTOR

AI / DM

BUDDY

DIVE NO

DATE

DIVE GROUP

WEATHER CONDITIONS

WEATHER CONDITIONS

START
bar / psi

END
bar / psi

LOCATION

TIME IN

TIME OUT

:

:

DIVE TIME

:

AVERAGE DEPTH

MAX DEPTH

LOCATION

LOCATION NAME

COUNTRY

EQUIPMENT

ADDITIONAL NOTES

DIVE CENTER / RESORT STAMP

INSTRUCTOR   AI / DM   BUDDY

DIVE NO

DATE

DIVE GROUP

WEATHER CONDITIONS

WEATHER CONDITIONS

START
bar / psi

END
bar / psi

LOCATION

TIME IN

TIME OUT

:

:

DIVE TIME

:

AVERAGE DEPTH

MAX DEPTH

LOCATION

LOCATION NAME

COUNTRY

EQUIPMENT

ADDITIONAL NOTES

DIVE CENTER / RESORT STAMP

INSTRUCTOR   AI / DM   BUDDY

DIVE NO

DATE

DIVE GROUP

WEATHER CONDITIONS

WEATHER CONDITIONS

START
bar / psi

END
bar / psi

LOCATION

LOCATION NAME

COUNTRY

LOCATION

TIME IN

TIME OUT

:

:

DIVE TIME

:

AVERAGE DEPTH

MAX DEPTH

EQUIPMENT

ADDITIONAL NOTES

DIVE CENTER / RESORT STAMP

INSTRUCTOR

AI / DM

BUDDY

DIVE NO

DATE

DIVE GROUP

WEATHER CONDITIONS

Temperature ———

Wind ———

WEATHER CONDITIONS

START
bar / psi

———

END
bar / psi

———

LOCATION

LOCATION NAME

COUNTRY

LOCATION

TIME IN

:

TIME OUT

:

DIVE TIME

:

AVERAGE DEPTH

MAX DEPTH

EQUIPMENT

ADDITIONAL NOTES

DIVE CENTER / RESORT STAMP

INSTRUCTOR   AI / DM   BUDDY

DIVE NO

DATE

DIVE GROUP

WEATHER CONDITIONS

START
bar / psi

END
bar / psi

LOCATION

TIME IN

TIME OUT

DIVE TIME

AVERAGE DEPTH

MAX DEPTH

ADDITIONAL NOTES

WEATHER CONDITIONS

LOCATION

LOCATION NAME

COUNTRY

EQUIPMENT

DIVE CENTER / RESORT STAMP

INSTRUCTOR   AI / DM   BUDDY

DIVE NO

DATE

DIVE GROUP

WEATHER CONDITIONS

🌡 ——

🚩 ——

☀ ☁ 🌧 ⛈ ❄

☐ ☐ ☐ ☐ ☐

WEATHER CONDITIONS

START
bar / psi
——

END
bar / psi
——

LOCATION

TIME IN

:

TIME OUT

:

DIVE TIME

:

⌀ AVERAGE DEPTH

MAX DEPTH

LOCATION

📍 LOCATION NAME

🗺 COUNTRY

EQUIPMENT

ADDITIONAL NOTES

DIVE CENTER / RESORT STAMP

INSTRUCTOR

☐

AI / DM

☐

BUDDY

☐

DIVE NO

DATE

DIVE GROUP

WEATHER CONDITIONS

WEATHER CONDITIONS

START
bar / psi
_____

END
bar / psi
_____

LOCATION

LOCATION NAME

COUNTRY

LOCATION

TIME IN

TIME OUT

:

:

DIVE TIME

:

AVERAGE DEPTH

MAX DEPTH

EQUIPMENT

ADDITIONAL NOTES

DIVE CENTER / RESORT STAMP

INSTRUCTOR

AI / DM

BUDDY

DIVE NO

DATE

DIVE GROUP

WEATHER CONDITIONS

START
bar / psi

END
bar / psi

LOCATION

TIME IN

TIME OUT

:

:

DIVE TIME

:

AVERAGE DEPTH

MAX DEPTH

ADDITIONAL NOTES

WEATHER CONDITIONS

LOCATION

LOCATION NAME

COUNTRY

EQUIPMENT

DIVE CENTER / RESORT STAMP

INSTRUCTOR   AI / DM   BUDDY

DIVE NO

DATE

DIVE GROUP

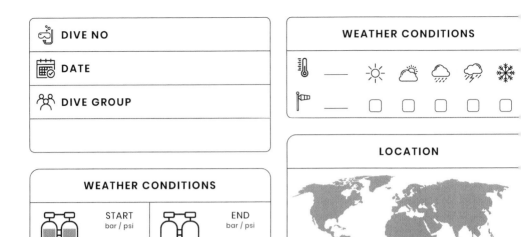

WEATHER CONDITIONS

WEATHER CONDITIONS

START
bar / psi

_____

END
bar / psi

_____

LOCATION

TIME IN

:

TIME OUT

:

DIVE TIME

:

AVERAGE DEPTH

MAX DEPTH

LOCATION

LOCATION NAME

COUNTRY

EQUIPMENT

ADDITIONAL NOTES

DIVE CENTER / RESORT STAMP

INSTRUCTOR

AI / DM

BUDDY

DIVE NO

DATE

DIVE GROUP

WEATHER CONDITIONS

---

bar / psi

WEATHER CONDITIONS

START bar / psi	END bar / psi
_____	_____

LOCATION

TIME IN

TIME OUT

:

:

DIVE TIME

:

AVERAGE DEPTH

MAX DEPTH

LOCATION

LOCATION NAME

COUNTRY

EQUIPMENT

ADDITIONAL NOTES

DIVE CENTER / RESORT STAMP

INSTRUCTOR   AI / DM   BUDDY

DIVE NO

DATE

DIVE GROUP

WEATHER CONDITIONS

WEATHER CONDITIONS

START
bar / psi

END
bar / psi

LOCATION

TIME IN

TIME OUT

:

:

DIVE TIME

:

AVERAGE DEPTH

MAX DEPTH

LOCATION

LOCATION NAME

COUNTRY

EQUIPMENT

ADDITIONAL NOTES

DIVE CENTER / RESORT STAMP

INSTRUCTOR

AI / DM

BUDDY

DIVE NO

DATE

DIVE GROUP

WEATHER CONDITIONS

START
bar / psi

END
bar / psi

LOCATION

TIME IN

TIME OUT

:

:

DIVE TIME

:

AVERAGE DEPTH

MAX DEPTH

WEATHER CONDITIONS

LOCATION

LOCATION NAME

COUNTRY

EQUIPMENT

ADDITIONAL NOTES

DIVE CENTER / RESORT STAMP

INSTRUCTOR

AI / DM

BUDDY

DIVE NO

DATE

DIVE GROUP

WEATHER CONDITIONS

☀ ⛅ ☁ ⛈ ❄
☐ ☐ ☐ ☐ ☐

LOCATION

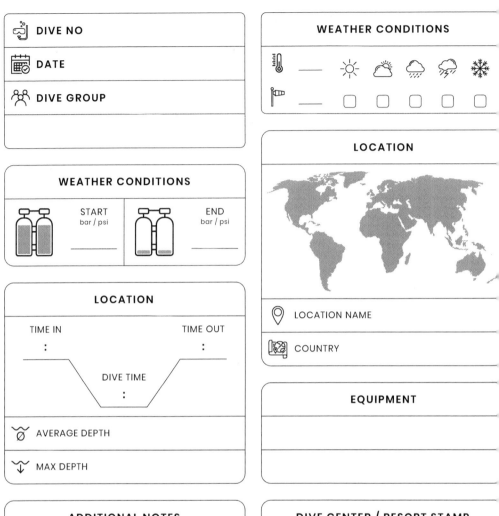

◎ LOCATION NAME

COUNTRY

WEATHER CONDITIONS

START bar / psi	END bar / psi

LOCATION

TIME IN

:

TIME OUT

:

DIVE TIME

:

AVERAGE DEPTH

MAX DEPTH

EQUIPMENT

ADDITIONAL NOTES

DIVE CENTER / RESORT STAMP

INSTRUCTOR	AI / DM	BUDDY
☐	☐	☐

DIVE NO

DATE

DIVE GROUP

WEATHER CONDITIONS

START
bar / psi

END
bar / psi

WEATHER CONDITIONS

LOCATION

TIME IN

TIME OUT

DIVE TIME

AVERAGE DEPTH

MAX DEPTH

LOCATION

LOCATION NAME

COUNTRY

EQUIPMENT

ADDITIONAL NOTES

DIVE CENTER / RESORT STAMP

INSTRUCTOR

AI / DM

BUDDY

DIVE NO

DATE

DIVE GROUP

WEATHER CONDITIONS

WEATHER CONDITIONS

START
bar / psi

END
bar / psi

LOCATION

TIME IN

TIME OUT

:

:

DIVE TIME

:

AVERAGE DEPTH

MAX DEPTH

LOCATION

LOCATION NAME

COUNTRY

EQUIPMENT

ADDITIONAL NOTES

DIVE CENTER / RESORT STAMP

INSTRUCTOR

AI / DM

BUDDY

DIVE NO

DATE

DIVE GROUP

WEATHER CONDITIONS

WEATHER CONDITIONS

START
bar / psi

END
bar / psi

LOCATION

TIME IN

TIME OUT

:

:

DIVE TIME

:

AVERAGE DEPTH

MAX DEPTH

LOCATION

LOCATION NAME

COUNTRY

EQUIPMENT

ADDITIONAL NOTES

DIVE CENTER / RESORT STAMP

INSTRUCTOR

AI / DM

BUDDY

DIVE NO

DATE

DIVE GROUP

WEATHER CONDITIONS

	START bar / psi		END bar / psi

LOCATION

TIME IN

TIME OUT

:

:

DIVE TIME

:

AVERAGE DEPTH

MAX DEPTH

ADDITIONAL NOTES

WEATHER CONDITIONS

LOCATION

LOCATION NAME

COUNTRY

EQUIPMENT

DIVE CENTER / RESORT STAMP

INSTRUCTOR   AI / DM   BUDDY

DIVE NO

DATE

DIVE GROUP

WEATHER CONDITIONS

START
bar / psi

END
bar / psi

WEATHER CONDITIONS

LOCATION

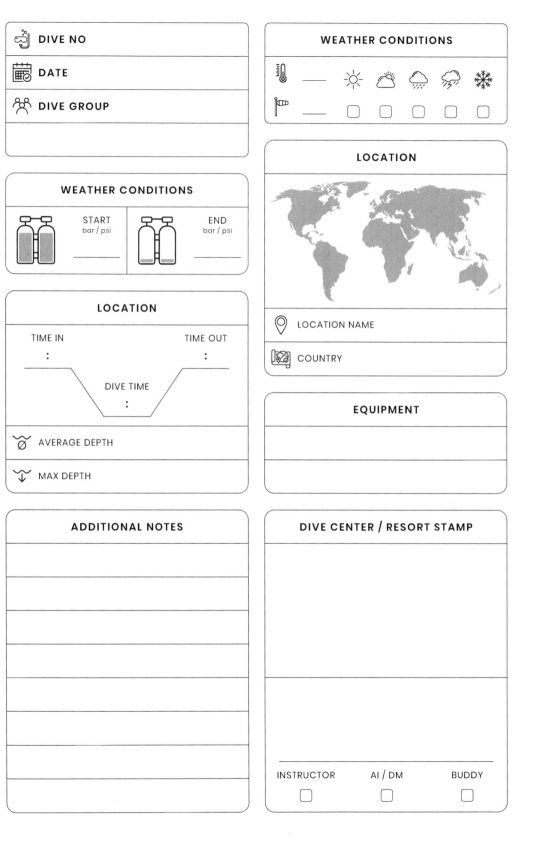

LOCATION NAME

COUNTRY

LOCATION

TIME IN

TIME OUT

:   :

DIVE TIME

:

AVERAGE DEPTH

MAX DEPTH

EQUIPMENT

ADDITIONAL NOTES

DIVE CENTER / RESORT STAMP

INSTRUCTOR   AI / DM   BUDDY

DIVE NO

DATE

DIVE GROUP

WEATHER CONDITIONS

START
bar / psi

END
bar / psi

LOCATION

TIME IN

TIME OUT

:

:

DIVE TIME

:

AVERAGE DEPTH

MAX DEPTH

ADDITIONAL NOTES

WEATHER CONDITIONS

LOCATION

LOCATION NAME

COUNTRY

EQUIPMENT

DIVE CENTER / RESORT STAMP

INSTRUCTOR

AI / DM

BUDDY

DIVE NO

DATE

DIVE GROUP

WEATHER CONDITIONS

WEATHER CONDITIONS

START
bar / psi

END
bar / psi

LOCATION

TIME IN

TIME OUT

:

:

DIVE TIME

:

AVERAGE DEPTH

MAX DEPTH

LOCATION

LOCATION NAME

COUNTRY

EQUIPMENT

ADDITIONAL NOTES

DIVE CENTER / RESORT STAMP

INSTRUCTOR

AI / DM

BUDDY

DIVE NO

DATE

DIVE GROUP

WEATHER CONDITIONS

WEATHER CONDITIONS

START
bar / psi

END
bar / psi

LOCATION

TIME IN

TIME OUT

:

:

DIVE TIME

:

AVERAGE DEPTH

MAX DEPTH

ADDITIONAL NOTES

LOCATION

LOCATION NAME

COUNTRY

EQUIPMENT

DIVE CENTER / RESORT STAMP

INSTRUCTOR

AI / DM

BUDDY

DIVE NO

DATE

DIVE GROUP

WEATHER CONDITIONS

WEATHER CONDITIONS

START
bar / psi

END
bar / psi

LOCATION

LOCATION NAME

COUNTRY

LOCATION

TIME IN

TIME OUT

:

:

DIVE TIME

:

AVERAGE DEPTH

MAX DEPTH

EQUIPMENT

ADDITIONAL NOTES

DIVE CENTER / RESORT STAMP

INSTRUCTOR

AI / DM

BUDDY

DIVE NO

DATE

DIVE GROUP

WEATHER CONDITIONS

WEATHER CONDITIONS

START
bar / psi

END
bar / psi

LOCATION

TIME IN

TIME OUT

:

:

DIVE TIME

:

AVERAGE DEPTH

MAX DEPTH

LOCATION

LOCATION NAME

COUNTRY

EQUIPMENT

ADDITIONAL NOTES

DIVE CENTER / RESORT STAMP

INSTRUCTOR

AI / DM

BUDDY

DIVE NO

DATE

DIVE GROUP

WEATHER CONDITIONS

WEATHER CONDITIONS

START
bar / psi

END
bar / psi

LOCATION

LOCATION NAME

COUNTRY

LOCATION

TIME IN

TIME OUT

:

:

DIVE TIME

:

AVERAGE DEPTH

MAX DEPTH

EQUIPMENT

ADDITIONAL NOTES

DIVE CENTER / RESORT STAMP

INSTRUCTOR

AI / DM

BUDDY

DIVE NO

DATE

DIVE GROUP

WEATHER CONDITIONS

START
bar / psi

END
bar / psi

LOCATION

TIME IN

TIME OUT

:

:

DIVE TIME

:

AVERAGE DEPTH

MAX DEPTH

ADDITIONAL NOTES

WEATHER CONDITIONS

LOCATION

LOCATION NAME

COUNTRY

EQUIPMENT

DIVE CENTER / RESORT STAMP

INSTRUCTOR

AI / DM

BUDDY

DIVE NO

DATE

DIVE GROUP

WEATHER CONDITIONS

WEATHER CONDITIONS

START
bar / psi

END
bar / psi

LOCATION

LOCATION NAME

COUNTRY

LOCATION

TIME IN

TIME OUT

:

:

DIVE TIME

:

AVERAGE DEPTH

MAX DEPTH

EQUIPMENT

ADDITIONAL NOTES

DIVE CENTER / RESORT STAMP

INSTRUCTOR

AI / DM

BUDDY

DIVE NO

DATE

DIVE GROUP

WEATHER CONDITIONS

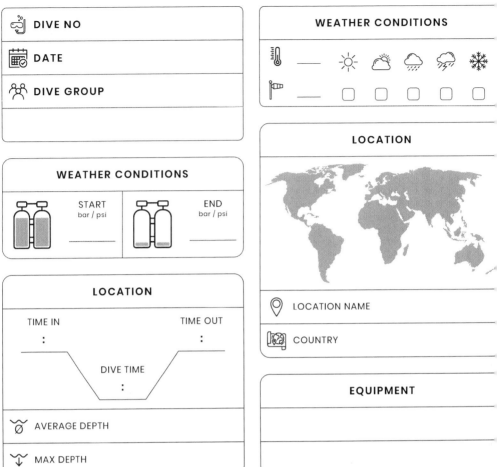

WEATHER CONDITIONS

START
bar / psi

END
bar / psi

LOCATION

TIME IN

TIME OUT

:

:

DIVE TIME

:

AVERAGE DEPTH

MAX DEPTH

LOCATION

LOCATION NAME

COUNTRY

EQUIPMENT

ADDITIONAL NOTES

DIVE CENTER / RESORT STAMP

INSTRUCTOR

AI / DM

BUDDY

DIVE NO

DATE

DIVE GROUP

WEATHER CONDITIONS

WEATHER CONDITIONS

START
bar / psi

END
bar / psi

LOCATION

TIME IN

TIME OUT

:

:

DIVE TIME

:

AVERAGE DEPTH

MAX DEPTH

LOCATION

LOCATION NAME

COUNTRY

EQUIPMENT

ADDITIONAL NOTES

DIVE CENTER / RESORT STAMP

INSTRUCTOR

AI / DM

BUDDY

DIVE NO

DATE

DIVE GROUP

WEATHER CONDITIONS

START
bar / psi

END
bar / psi

WEATHER CONDITIONS

LOCATION

TIME IN

TIME OUT

DIVE TIME

AVERAGE DEPTH

MAX DEPTH

LOCATION

LOCATION NAME

COUNTRY

EQUIPMENT

ADDITIONAL NOTES

DIVE CENTER / RESORT STAMP

INSTRUCTOR

AI / DM

BUDDY

DIVE NO

DATE

DIVE GROUP

WEATHER CONDITIONS

WEATHER CONDITIONS

START
bar / psi

END
bar / psi

LOCATION

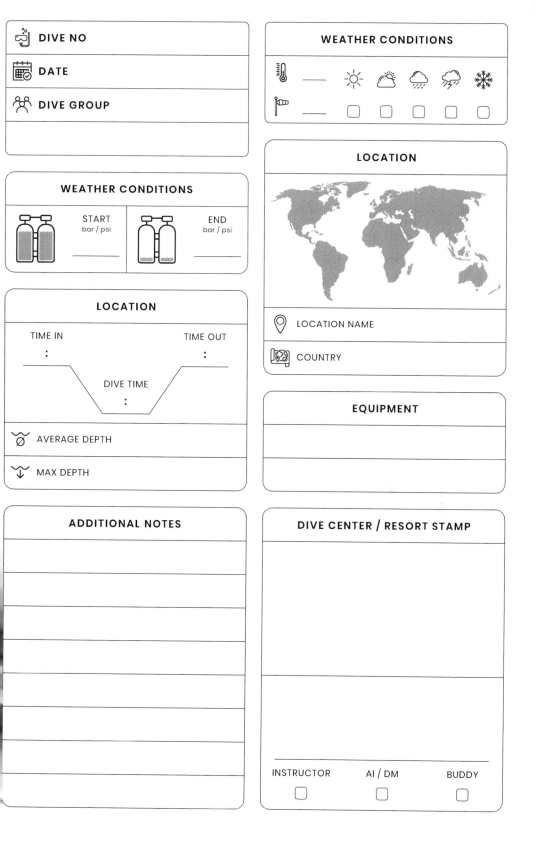

LOCATION NAME

COUNTRY

LOCATION

TIME IN

TIME OUT

:

:

DIVE TIME

:

AVERAGE DEPTH

MAX DEPTH

EQUIPMENT

ADDITIONAL NOTES

DIVE CENTER / RESORT STAMP

INSTRUCTOR

AI / DM

BUDDY

DIVE NO

DATE

DIVE GROUP

WEATHER CONDITIONS

WEATHER CONDITIONS

START
bar / psi

END
bar / psi

LOCATION

TIME IN

TIME OUT

:

:

DIVE TIME

:

AVERAGE DEPTH

MAX DEPTH

LOCATION

LOCATION NAME

COUNTRY

EQUIPMENT

ADDITIONAL NOTES

DIVE CENTER / RESORT STAMP

INSTRUCTOR

AI / DM

BUDDY

DIVE NO

DATE

DIVE GROUP

WEATHER CONDITIONS

START
bar / psi

END
bar / psi

LOCATION

TIME IN

TIME OUT

DIVE TIME

AVERAGE DEPTH

MAX DEPTH

ADDITIONAL NOTES

WEATHER CONDITIONS

LOCATION

LOCATION NAME

COUNTRY

EQUIPMENT

DIVE CENTER / RESORT STAMP

INSTRUCTOR   AI / DM   BUDDY

DIVE NO

DATE

DIVE GROUP

WEATHER CONDITIONS

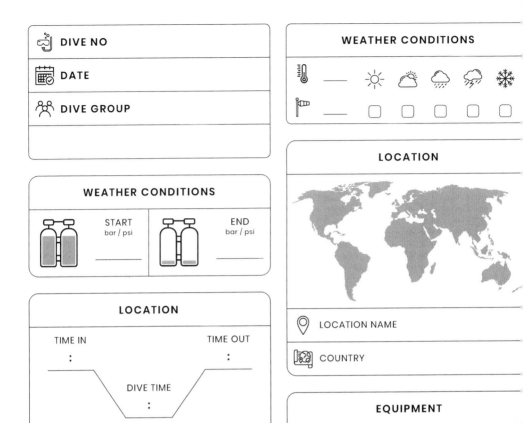

WEATHER CONDITIONS

START
bar / psi

END
bar / psi

LOCATION

TIME IN

TIME OUT

:

:

DIVE TIME

:

AVERAGE DEPTH

MAX DEPTH

LOCATION

LOCATION NAME

COUNTRY

EQUIPMENT

ADDITIONAL NOTES

DIVE CENTER / RESORT STAMP

INSTRUCTOR

AI / DM

BUDDY

DIVE NO

DATE

DIVE GROUP

WEATHER CONDITIONS

WEATHER CONDITIONS

START
bar / psi

END
bar / psi

LOCATION

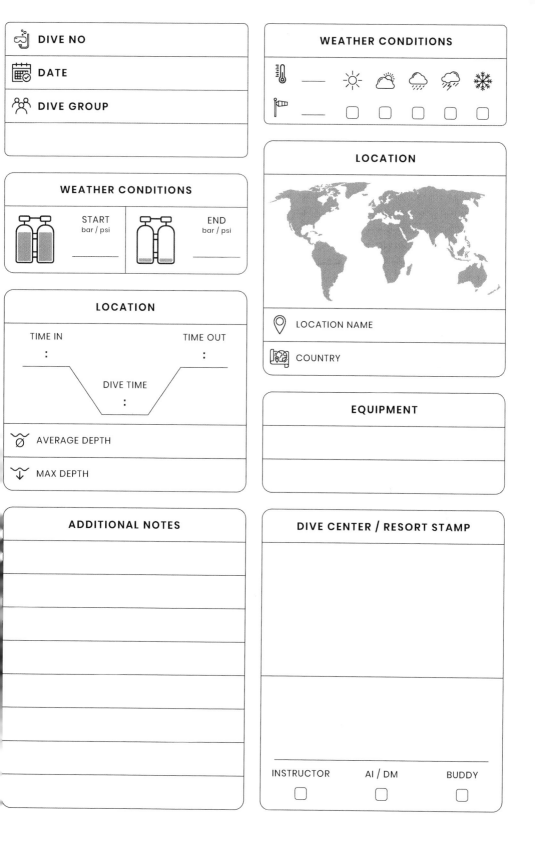

LOCATION NAME

COUNTRY

LOCATION

TIME IN

TIME OUT

:

:

DIVE TIME

:

AVERAGE DEPTH

MAX DEPTH

EQUIPMENT

ADDITIONAL NOTES

DIVE CENTER / RESORT STAMP

INSTRUCTOR

AI / DM

BUDDY

DIVE NO

DATE

DIVE GROUP

WEATHER CONDITIONS

WEATHER CONDITIONS

	START bar / psi		END bar / psi

LOCATION

TIME IN

TIME OUT

: :

DIVE TIME

:

AVERAGE DEPTH

MAX DEPTH

LOCATION

LOCATION NAME

COUNTRY

EQUIPMENT

ADDITIONAL NOTES

DIVE CENTER / RESORT STAMP

INSTRUCTOR   AI / DM   BUDDY

DIVE NO

DATE

DIVE GROUP

WEATHER CONDITIONS

——

WEATHER CONDITIONS

START bar / psi		END bar / psi
———		———

LOCATION

LOCATION NAME

COUNTRY

LOCATION

TIME IN

:

TIME OUT

:

DIVE TIME

:

AVERAGE DEPTH

MAX DEPTH

EQUIPMENT

ADDITIONAL NOTES

DIVE CENTER / RESORT STAMP

INSTRUCTOR   AI / DM   BUDDY

DIVE NO

DATE

DIVE GROUP

WEATHER CONDITIONS

WEATHER CONDITIONS

START
bar / psi

END
bar / psi

LOCATION

LOCATION

TIME IN

TIME OUT

:

:

DIVE TIME

:

AVERAGE DEPTH

MAX DEPTH

LOCATION NAME

COUNTRY

EQUIPMENT

ADDITIONAL NOTES

DIVE CENTER / RESORT STAMP

INSTRUCTOR

AI / DM

BUDDY

DIVE NO

DATE

DIVE GROUP

WEATHER CONDITIONS

WEATHER CONDITIONS

START
bar / psi

END
bar / psi

LOCATION

TIME IN

TIME OUT

:

:

DIVE TIME

:

AVERAGE DEPTH

MAX DEPTH

LOCATION

LOCATION NAME

COUNTRY

EQUIPMENT

ADDITIONAL NOTES

DIVE CENTER / RESORT STAMP

INSTRUCTOR

AI / DM

BUDDY

DIVE NO

DATE

DIVE GROUP

WEATHER CONDITIONS

START
bar / psi

END
bar / psi

LOCATION

TIME IN

TIME OUT

:

:

DIVE TIME

:

AVERAGE DEPTH

MAX DEPTH

WEATHER CONDITIONS

LOCATION

LOCATION NAME

COUNTRY

EQUIPMENT

ADDITIONAL NOTES

DIVE CENTER / RESORT STAMP

INSTRUCTOR

AI / DM

BUDDY

DIVE NO

DATE

DIVE GROUP

WEATHER CONDITIONS

☀ ⛅ 🌧 ⛈ ❄

☐ ☐ ☐ ☐ ☐

WEATHER CONDITIONS

START
bar / psi

END
bar / psi

LOCATION

LOCATION NAME

COUNTRY

LOCATION

TIME IN :

TIME OUT :

DIVE TIME :

AVERAGE DEPTH

MAX DEPTH

EQUIPMENT

ADDITIONAL NOTES

DIVE CENTER / RESORT STAMP

INSTRUCTOR ☐

AI / DM ☐

BUDDY ☐

DIVE NO

DATE

DIVE GROUP

WEATHER CONDITIONS

START
bar / psi

END
bar / psi

LOCATION

TIME IN

TIME OUT

:

:

DIVE TIME

:

AVERAGE DEPTH

MAX DEPTH

ADDITIONAL NOTES

WEATHER CONDITIONS

LOCATION

LOCATION NAME

COUNTRY

EQUIPMENT

DIVE CENTER / RESORT STAMP

INSTRUCTOR

AI / DM

BUDDY

DIVE NO

DATE

DIVE GROUP

WEATHER CONDITIONS

WEATHER CONDITIONS

START
bar / psi

END
bar / psi

LOCATION

TIME IN

TIME OUT

:

:

DIVE TIME

:

AVERAGE DEPTH

MAX DEPTH

LOCATION

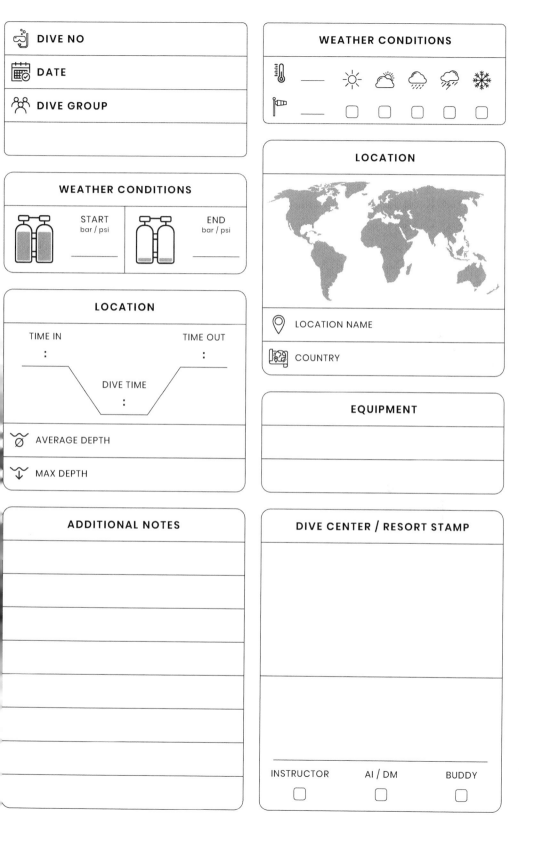

LOCATION NAME

COUNTRY

EQUIPMENT

ADDITIONAL NOTES

DIVE CENTER / RESORT STAMP

INSTRUCTOR

AI / DM

BUDDY

DIVE NO

DATE

DIVE GROUP

WEATHER CONDITIONS

WEATHER CONDITIONS

START
bar / psi

END
bar / psi

LOCATION

TIME IN

TIME OUT

:

:

DIVE TIME

:

AVERAGE DEPTH

MAX DEPTH

LOCATION

LOCATION NAME

COUNTRY

EQUIPMENT

ADDITIONAL NOTES

DIVE CENTER / RESORT STAMP

INSTRUCTOR

AI / DM

BUDDY

DIVE NO

DATE

DIVE GROUP

WEATHER CONDITIONS

WEATHER CONDITIONS

START
bar / psi

END
bar / psi

LOCATION

TIME IN

TIME OUT

DIVE TIME

AVERAGE DEPTH

MAX DEPTH

LOCATION

LOCATION NAME

COUNTRY

EQUIPMENT

ADDITIONAL NOTES

DIVE CENTER / RESORT STAMP

INSTRUCTOR

AI / DM

BUDDY

DIVE NO

DATE

DIVE GROUP

WEATHER CONDITIONS

WEATHER CONDITIONS

START
bar / psi

END
bar / psi

LOCATION

TIME IN

TIME OUT

:

:

DIVE TIME

:

AVERAGE DEPTH

MAX DEPTH

LOCATION

LOCATION NAME

COUNTRY

EQUIPMENT

ADDITIONAL NOTES

DIVE CENTER / RESORT STAMP

INSTRUCTOR

AI / DM

BUDDY

DIVE NO

DATE

DIVE GROUP

WEATHER CONDITIONS

WEATHER CONDITIONS

START
bar / psi

END
bar / psi

LOCATION

TIME IN

TIME OUT

:

:

DIVE TIME

:

AVERAGE DEPTH

MAX DEPTH

LOCATION

LOCATION NAME

COUNTRY

EQUIPMENT

ADDITIONAL NOTES

DIVE CENTER / RESORT STAMP

INSTRUCTOR   AI / DM   BUDDY

DIVE NO

DATE

DIVE GROUP

WEATHER CONDITIONS

WEATHER CONDITIONS

START
bar / psi

END
bar / psi

LOCATION

TIME IN

TIME OUT

DIVE TIME

AVERAGE DEPTH

MAX DEPTH

LOCATION

LOCATION NAME

COUNTRY

EQUIPMENT

ADDITIONAL NOTES

DIVE CENTER / RESORT STAMP

INSTRUCTOR   AI / DM   BUDDY

DIVE NO

DATE

DIVE GROUP

WEATHER CONDITIONS

WEATHER CONDITIONS

START
bar / psi

END
bar / psi

LOCATION

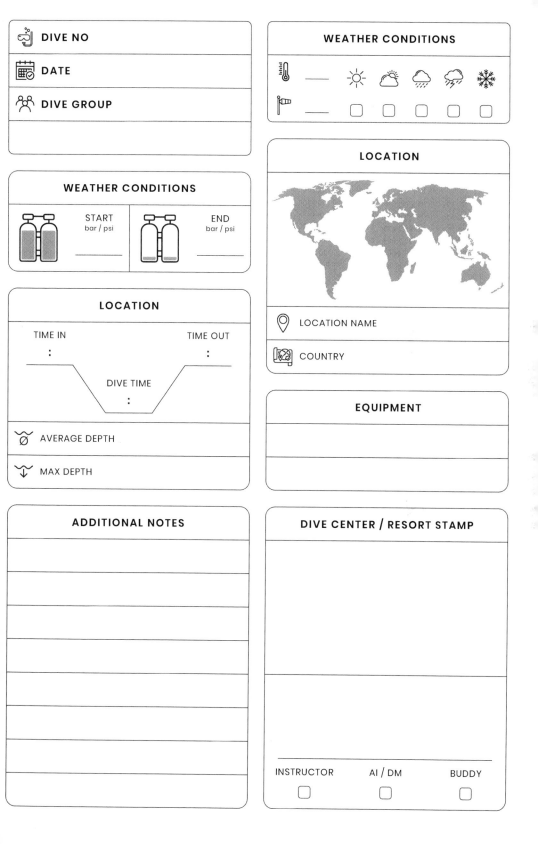

LOCATION NAME

COUNTRY

LOCATION

TIME IN

TIME OUT

:

:

DIVE TIME

:

AVERAGE DEPTH

MAX DEPTH

EQUIPMENT

ADDITIONAL NOTES

DIVE CENTER / RESORT STAMP

INSTRUCTOR

AI / DM

BUDDY

DIVE NO

DATE

DIVE GROUP

WEATHER CONDITIONS

WEATHER CONDITIONS

START
bar / psi

END
bar / psi

LOCATION

TIME IN

TIME OUT

:

:

DIVE TIME

:

AVERAGE DEPTH

MAX DEPTH

LOCATION

LOCATION NAME

COUNTRY

EQUIPMENT

ADDITIONAL NOTES

DIVE CENTER / RESORT STAMP

INSTRUCTOR

AI / DM

BUDDY

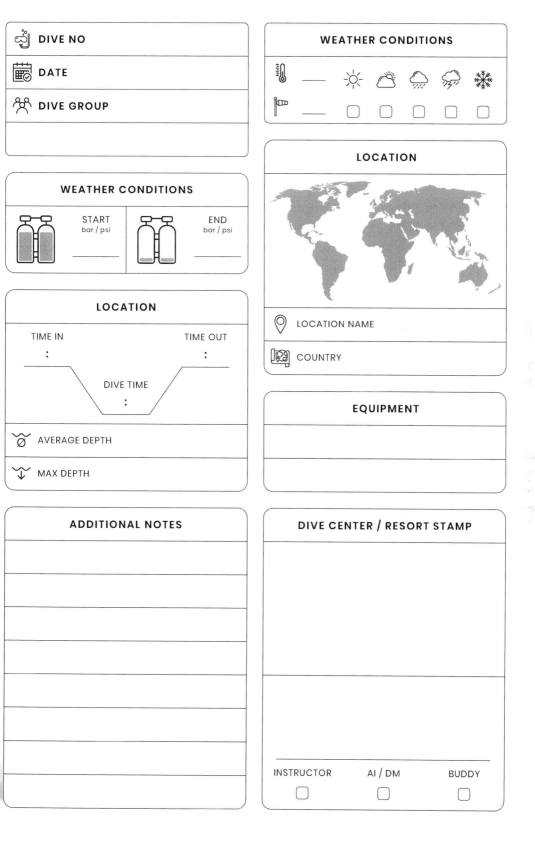

DIVE NO

DATE

DIVE GROUP

WEATHER CONDITIONS

WEATHER CONDITIONS

START
bar / psi

END
bar / psi

LOCATION

TIME IN

TIME OUT

:

:

DIVE TIME

:

AVERAGE DEPTH

MAX DEPTH

LOCATION

LOCATION NAME

COUNTRY

EQUIPMENT

ADDITIONAL NOTES

DIVE CENTER / RESORT STAMP

INSTRUCTOR

AI / DM

BUDDY

DIVE NO

DATE

DIVE GROUP

WEATHER CONDITIONS

WEATHER CONDITIONS

START
bar / psi

END
bar / psi

LOCATION

TIME IN

TIME OUT

:

:

DIVE TIME

:

AVERAGE DEPTH

MAX DEPTH

LOCATION

LOCATION NAME

COUNTRY

EQUIPMENT

ADDITIONAL NOTES

DIVE CENTER / RESORT STAMP

INSTRUCTOR

AI / DM

BUDDY

DIVE NO

DATE

DIVE GROUP

WEATHER CONDITIONS

WEATHER CONDITIONS

START
bar / psi

END
bar / psi

LOCATION

TIME IN

TIME OUT

:

:

DIVE TIME

:

AVERAGE DEPTH

MAX DEPTH

LOCATION

LOCATION NAME

COUNTRY

EQUIPMENT

ADDITIONAL NOTES

DIVE CENTER / RESORT STAMP

INSTRUCTOR   AI / DM   BUDDY

DIVE NO

DATE

DIVE GROUP

WEATHER CONDITIONS

WEATHER CONDITIONS

START bar / psi	END bar / psi

LOCATION

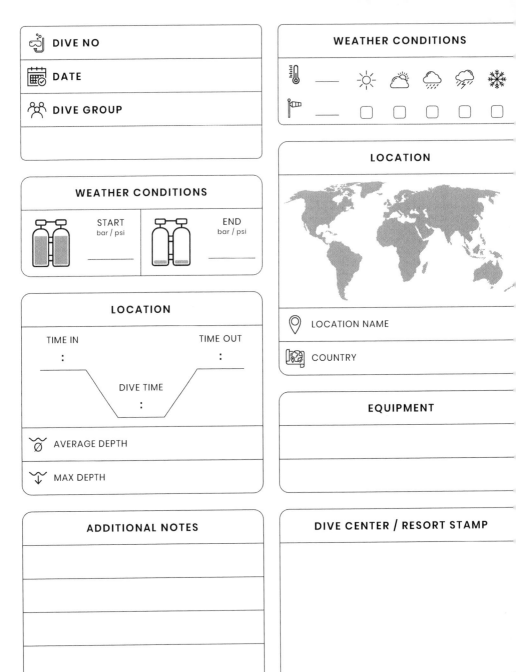

LOCATION NAME

COUNTRY

LOCATION

TIME IN

:

TIME OUT

:

DIVE TIME

:

AVERAGE DEPTH

MAX DEPTH

EQUIPMENT

ADDITIONAL NOTES

DIVE CENTER / RESORT STAMP

INSTRUCTOR

AI / DM

BUDDY

DIVE NO

DATE

DIVE GROUP

WEATHER CONDITIONS

WEATHER CONDITIONS

START
bar / psi

END
bar / psi

LOCATION

TIME IN

TIME OUT

:

:

DIVE TIME

:

AVERAGE DEPTH

MAX DEPTH

LOCATION

LOCATION NAME

COUNTRY

EQUIPMENT

ADDITIONAL NOTES

DIVE CENTER / RESORT STAMP

INSTRUCTOR

AI / DM

BUDDY

DIVE NO

DATE

DIVE GROUP

WEATHER CONDITIONS

WEATHER CONDITIONS

START bar / psi	END bar / psi

LOCATION

LOCATION NAME

COUNTRY

LOCATION

TIME IN

TIME OUT

DIVE TIME

AVERAGE DEPTH

MAX DEPTH

EQUIPMENT

ADDITIONAL NOTES

DIVE CENTER / RESORT STAMP

INSTRUCTOR | AI / DM | BUDDY

DIVE NO

DATE

DIVE GROUP

WEATHER CONDITIONS

_____

_____

WEATHER CONDITIONS

START bar / psi	END bar / psi
_____	_____

LOCATION

LOCATION NAME

COUNTRY

LOCATION

TIME IN
:

TIME OUT
:

DIVE TIME
:

AVERAGE DEPTH

MAX DEPTH

EQUIPMENT

ADDITIONAL NOTES

DIVE CENTER / RESORT STAMP

_____

INSTRUCTOR   AI / DM   BUDDY

DIVE NO

DATE

DIVE GROUP

WEATHER CONDITIONS

START
bar / psi

END
bar / psi

LOCATION

TIME IN

TIME OUT

DIVE TIME

AVERAGE DEPTH

MAX DEPTH

WEATHER CONDITIONS

LOCATION

LOCATION NAME

COUNTRY

EQUIPMENT

ADDITIONAL NOTES

DIVE CENTER / RESORT STAMP

INSTRUCTOR

AI / DM

BUDDY

DIVE NO

DATE

DIVE GROUP

WEATHER CONDITIONS

WEATHER CONDITIONS

START
bar / psi

END
bar / psi

LOCATION

TIME IN

TIME OUT

:

:

DIVE TIME

:

AVERAGE DEPTH

MAX DEPTH

LOCATION

LOCATION NAME

COUNTRY

EQUIPMENT

ADDITIONAL NOTES

DIVE CENTER / RESORT STAMP

INSTRUCTOR

AI / DM

BUDDY

DIVE NO

DATE

DIVE GROUP

WEATHER CONDITIONS

START
bar / psi

END
bar / psi

LOCATION

TIME IN

TIME OUT

:

:

DIVE TIME

:

AVERAGE DEPTH

MAX DEPTH

WEATHER CONDITIONS

LOCATION

LOCATION NAME

COUNTRY

EQUIPMENT

ADDITIONAL NOTES

DIVE CENTER / RESORT STAMP

INSTRUCTOR

AI / DM

BUDDY

DIVE NO

DATE

DIVE GROUP

WEATHER CONDITIONS

WEATHER CONDITIONS

START
bar / psi

END
bar / psi

LOCATION

TIME IN

TIME OUT

:

:

DIVE TIME

:

AVERAGE DEPTH

MAX DEPTH

LOCATION

LOCATION NAME

COUNTRY

EQUIPMENT

ADDITIONAL NOTES

DIVE CENTER / RESORT STAMP

INSTRUCTOR

AI / DM

BUDDY

DIVE NO

DATE

DIVE GROUP

WEATHER CONDITIONS

WEATHER CONDITIONS

START bar / psi	END bar / psi
_____	_____

LOCATION

TIME IN

:

TIME OUT

:

DIVE TIME

:

AVERAGE DEPTH

MAX DEPTH

LOCATION

LOCATION NAME

COUNTRY

EQUIPMENT

ADDITIONAL NOTES

DIVE CENTER / RESORT STAMP

INSTRUCTOR   AI / DM   BUDDY

DIVE NO

DATE

DIVE GROUP

WEATHER CONDITIONS

WEATHER CONDITIONS

START
bar / psi

END
bar / psi

LOCATION

LOCATION NAME

COUNTRY

LOCATION

TIME IN

TIME OUT

:

:

DIVE TIME

:

AVERAGE DEPTH

MAX DEPTH

EQUIPMENT

ADDITIONAL NOTES

DIVE CENTER / RESORT STAMP

INSTRUCTOR   AI / DM   BUDDY

DIVE NO

DATE

DIVE GROUP

WEATHER CONDITIONS

WEATHER CONDITIONS

START
bar / psi

END
bar / psi

LOCATION

TIME IN

TIME OUT

:

:

DIVE TIME

:

AVERAGE DEPTH

MAX DEPTH

LOCATION

LOCATION NAME

COUNTRY

EQUIPMENT

ADDITIONAL NOTES

DIVE CENTER / RESORT STAMP

INSTRUCTOR

AI / DM

BUDDY

DIVE NO

DATE

DIVE GROUP

WEATHER CONDITIONS

WEATHER CONDITIONS

START
bar / psi

END
bar / psi

LOCATION

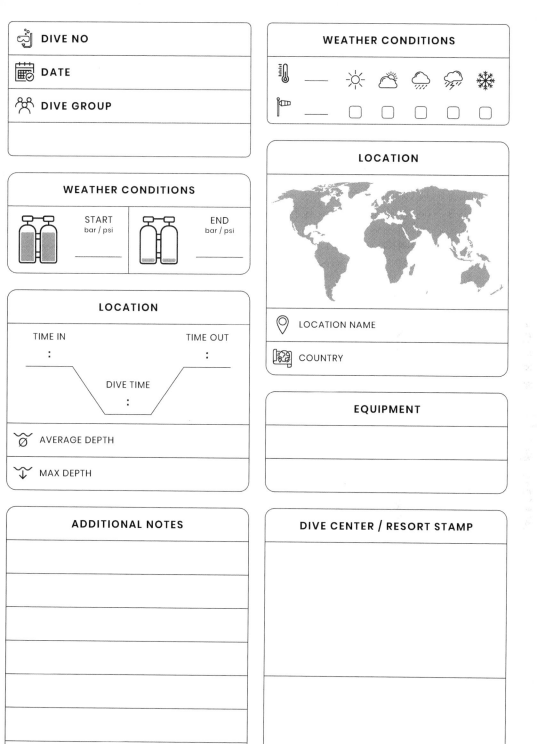

LOCATION NAME

COUNTRY

LOCATION

TIME IN

TIME OUT

:

:

DIVE TIME

:

AVERAGE DEPTH

MAX DEPTH

EQUIPMENT

ADDITIONAL NOTES

DIVE CENTER / RESORT STAMP

INSTRUCTOR   AI / DM   BUDDY

DIVE NO

DATE

DIVE GROUP

WEATHER CONDITIONS

WEATHER CONDITIONS

START
bar / psi

_____

END
bar / psi

_____

LOCATION

TIME IN

:

TIME OUT

:

DIVE TIME

:

AVERAGE DEPTH

MAX DEPTH

LOCATION

LOCATION NAME

COUNTRY

EQUIPMENT

ADDITIONAL NOTES

DIVE CENTER / RESORT STAMP

INSTRUCTOR

AI / DM

BUDDY

DIVE NO

DATE

DIVE GROUP

WEATHER CONDITIONS

WEATHER CONDITIONS

START
bar / psi

END
bar / psi

LOCATION

TIME IN

TIME OUT

:

:

DIVE TIME

:

AVERAGE DEPTH

MAX DEPTH

LOCATION

LOCATION NAME

COUNTRY

EQUIPMENT

ADDITIONAL NOTES

DIVE CENTER / RESORT STAMP

INSTRUCTOR

AI / DM

BUDDY

DIVE NO

DATE

DIVE GROUP

WEATHER CONDITIONS

WEATHER CONDITIONS

START
bar / psi

END
bar / psi

LOCATION

TIME IN

TIME OUT

:

:

DIVE TIME

:

AVERAGE DEPTH

MAX DEPTH

LOCATION

LOCATION NAME

COUNTRY

EQUIPMENT

ADDITIONAL NOTES

DIVE CENTER / RESORT STAMP

INSTRUCTOR

AI / DM

BUDDY

DIVE NO

DATE

DIVE GROUP

WEATHER CONDITIONS

WEATHER CONDITIONS

START
bar / psi

END
bar / psi

LOCATION

TIME IN

:

TIME OUT

:

DIVE TIME

:

AVERAGE DEPTH

MAX DEPTH

LOCATION

LOCATION NAME

COUNTRY

EQUIPMENT

ADDITIONAL NOTES

DIVE CENTER / RESORT STAMP

INSTRUCTOR

AI / DM

BUDDY

DIVE NO

DATE

DIVE GROUP

WEATHER CONDITIONS

START
bar / psi
_____

END
bar / psi
_____

LOCATION

TIME IN

TIME OUT

:

:

DIVE TIME

:

AVERAGE DEPTH

MAX DEPTH

WEATHER CONDITIONS

_____

_____

LOCATION

LOCATION NAME

COUNTRY

EQUIPMENT

ADDITIONAL NOTES

DIVE CENTER / RESORT STAMP

INSTRUCTOR

AI / DM

BUDDY

DIVE NO

DATE

DIVE GROUP

WEATHER CONDITIONS

START
bar / psi

END
bar / psi

LOCATION

TIME IN

TIME OUT

:

:

DIVE TIME

:

AVERAGE DEPTH

MAX DEPTH

ADDITIONAL NOTES

WEATHER CONDITIONS

LOCATION

LOCATION NAME

COUNTRY

EQUIPMENT

DIVE CENTER / RESORT STAMP

INSTRUCTOR

AI / DM

BUDDY

DIVE NO

DATE

DIVE GROUP

WEATHER CONDITIONS

WEATHER CONDITIONS

START bar / psi	END bar / psi
_____	_____

LOCATION

TIME IN

:

TIME OUT

:

DIVE TIME

:

AVERAGE DEPTH

MAX DEPTH

LOCATION

LOCATION NAME

COUNTRY

EQUIPMENT

ADDITIONAL NOTES

DIVE CENTER / RESORT STAMP

INSTRUCTOR	AI / DM	BUDDY

DIVE NO

DATE

DIVE GROUP

WEATHER CONDITIONS

WEATHER CONDITIONS

START
bar / psi

END
bar / psi

LOCATION

LOCATION NAME

COUNTRY

LOCATION

TIME IN
:

TIME OUT
:

DIVE TIME
:

AVERAGE DEPTH

MAX DEPTH

EQUIPMENT

ADDITIONAL NOTES

DIVE CENTER / RESORT STAMP

INSTRUCTOR   AI / DM   BUDDY

DIVE NO

DATE

DIVE GROUP

WEATHER CONDITIONS

WEATHER CONDITIONS

START
bar / psi

END
bar / psi

LOCATION

TIME IN

TIME OUT

:

:

DIVE TIME

:

AVERAGE DEPTH

MAX DEPTH

LOCATION

LOCATION NAME

COUNTRY

EQUIPMENT

ADDITIONAL NOTES

DIVE CENTER / RESORT STAMP

INSTRUCTOR

AI / DM

BUDDY

DIVE NO

DATE

DIVE GROUP

WEATHER CONDITIONS

🌡 ____ ☀ ⛅ 🌧 ⛈ ❄
🚩 ____ ☐ ☐ ☐ ☐ ☐

WEATHER CONDITIONS

START
bar / psi
____

END
bar / psi
____

LOCATION

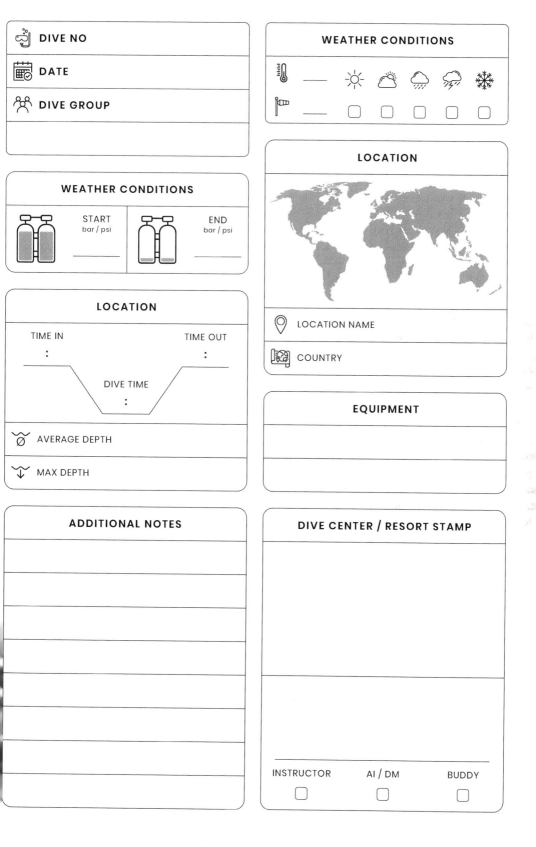

📍 LOCATION NAME

🗺 COUNTRY

LOCATION

TIME IN

:

TIME OUT

:

DIVE TIME

:

∅ AVERAGE DEPTH

MAX DEPTH

EQUIPMENT

ADDITIONAL NOTES

DIVE CENTER / RESORT STAMP

INSTRUCTOR
☐

AI / DM
☐

BUDDY
☐

DIVE NO

DATE

DIVE GROUP

WEATHER CONDITIONS

☀ ⛅ 🌧 ⛈ ❄

WEATHER CONDITIONS

START
bar / psi

END
bar / psi

LOCATION

LOCATION NAME

COUNTRY

LOCATION

TIME IN

TIME OUT

:   :

DIVE TIME

:

AVERAGE DEPTH

MAX DEPTH

EQUIPMENT

ADDITIONAL NOTES

DIVE CENTER / RESORT STAMP

INSTRUCTOR   AI / DM   BUDDY

DIVE NO

DATE

DIVE GROUP

WEATHER CONDITIONS

WEATHER CONDITIONS

START
bar / psi

END
bar / psi

LOCATION

TIME IN

TIME OUT

:

:

DIVE TIME

:

AVERAGE DEPTH

MAX DEPTH

LOCATION

LOCATION NAME

COUNTRY

EQUIPMENT

ADDITIONAL NOTES

DIVE CENTER / RESORT STAMP

INSTRUCTOR

AI / DM

BUDDY

DIVE NO

DATE

DIVE GROUP

WEATHER CONDITIONS

START
bar / psi

END
bar / psi

LOCATION

TIME IN

TIME OUT

:

:

DIVE TIME

:

AVERAGE DEPTH

MAX DEPTH

ADDITIONAL NOTES

WEATHER CONDITIONS

LOCATION

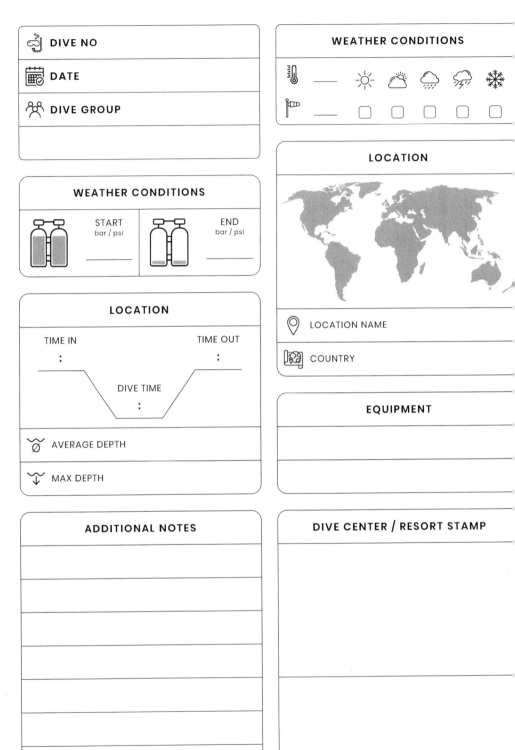

LOCATION NAME

COUNTRY

EQUIPMENT

DIVE CENTER / RESORT STAMP

INSTRUCTOR

AI / DM

BUDDY

DIVE NO

DATE

DIVE GROUP

WEATHER CONDITIONS

WEATHER CONDITIONS

START
bar / psi

END
bar / psi

LOCATION

TIME IN
:

TIME OUT
:

DIVE TIME
:

AVERAGE DEPTH

MAX DEPTH

LOCATION

LOCATION NAME

COUNTRY

EQUIPMENT

ADDITIONAL NOTES

DIVE CENTER / RESORT STAMP

INSTRUCTOR   AI / DM   BUDDY

DIVE NO

DATE

DIVE GROUP

WEATHER CONDITIONS

START
bar / psi

END
bar / psi

WEATHER CONDITIONS

LOCATION

TIME IN

TIME OUT

:

:

DIVE TIME

:

AVERAGE DEPTH

MAX DEPTH

LOCATION NAME

COUNTRY

EQUIPMENT

ADDITIONAL NOTES

DIVE CENTER / RESORT STAMP

INSTRUCTOR

AI / DM

BUDDY

Made in United States
Orlando, FL
11 July 2023

34974079R00067